D1442005

HAZEL RIDES AGAIN

Books by Ted Key

HAZEL

HERE'S HAZEL

IF YOU LIKE HAZEL

MANY HAPPY RETURNS

SO'M I

Ted Key

HAZEL RIDES AGAIN

A NEW SELECTION OF

HAZEL CARTOONS

With an Introduction by BEN HIBBS, Editor, *Saturday Evening Post*

NEW YORK E. P. DUTTON & CO., INC. 1955

The cartoons in this book have appeared in *The Saturday Evening Post*
and copyright by The Curtis Publishing Company as follows:
1952: pages 12, 16, 18, 35, 40, 47, 50, 52, 53, 56, 59, 60, 61, 62, 65, 66, 70, 71, 74, 76, 77, 79, 83, 86, 87, 91, 92, 97, 104, 106, 107, 109, 121, 124.
1953: pages 13, 16, 17, 19, 21, 22, 24, 29, 30, 31, 32, 37, 43, 46, 51, 58, 67, 68, 69, 72, 75, 79, 81, 85, 88, 89, 90, 91, 94, 95, 98, 99, 100, 101, 102, 108, 109, 111, 112, 113, 114, 115, 116, 118, 120, 122.
1954: pages (Endpaper, Jacket), 11, 14, 15, 20, 22, 23, 25, 26, 27, 28, 33, 34, 35, 36, 39, 41, 43, 44, 45, 48, 49, 55, 57, 61, 63, 64, 71, 73, 76, 78, 80, 82, 84, 88, 93, 96, 97, 98, 105, 117, 119.
1955: pages 15, 42, 50, 54, 82, 94, 103, 118, 125.

The Artist gratefully acknowledges permission granted by
The Curtis Publishing Company to reprint them.

Library of Congress Catalog Card Number: 55-9647

TO PETER

"Who'd like to play follow-the-leader?"

Introduction
by
Ben Hibbs, Editor
The Saturday Evening Post

The scene was the vast mess hall where nearly 3,000 midshipmen were eating their lunch. I had been invited by the Superintendent of the Naval Academy to spend a couple of days with him at Annapolis, and on this day he had suggested that I might enjoy having lunch with the midshipmen.

As the soup course was being consumed, several announcements were made over the loud-speaking system – one of them being that the Editor of *The Saturday Evening Post* was present that day at the head table. I rose and bowed. A few of the uniformed young men glanced casually in my direction, and there was a momentary break in the rhythmic clatter of the soup spoons, followed by a faint, polite spatter of applause. The "so what?" atmosphere was so thick you could have cut it with a knife.

About five minutes later, however – at no discernible signal that I could see – a profound silence fell over the whole hall. Obviously something was about to happen. And then it did. Nearly three thousand voices suddenly erupted into a roaring three cheers for Hazel! Hazel!! HAZEL!!!

If I had had any illusions about my own importance, it would have been a humbling experience. Long ago, however, I had concluded that an editor is merely a vague and shadowy figure to his audience. Our surveys had indicated that probably not more than one in five readers of the *Post* could give the name of the editor, whereas from 85 to 95 per cent could readily identify such star performers as Norman Rockwell and Clarence Budington Kelland and such popular features as Hazel.

The Hazel cartoon has been so highly popular with *Post* readers for so long – it became a regular, weekly feature in 1943 – that we no longer try to figure out what makes it tick. It is one of those phenomena that an editor takes on faith and includes in his blessings when he offers up an occasional prayer of thanks to the gods of Journalism.

Yet of course there are reasons for Hazel's popularity. An obvious one is that Ted Key is a skilled craftsman; entirely aside from the situations involved, his cartoons are funny to look at. Another reason which may be less obvious but perhaps is even more important is that in his Hazel cartoons Ted invariably deals with familiar, plausible situations rather than the preposterous. Like Norman Rockwell's cover paintings, Ted's cartoons have a common denominator for most of us. In fact, I have often said that Ted Key is the Rockwell of the cartoon world.

The overriding reason for Hazel's popularity, however, is that Ted Key is Ted Key – a gay and delightful guy with an impudent twinkle in his eye. Some humorists I know are, in private life, pretty dour people. But not Ted. He's like Hazel herself. And long may the two of them wave.

Ted Key
Ted Key

KINSEY
REPORT
Ted Key

1

"I know it's your room lady—you have to live in it, but I'd no more paint this room that dark color . . ."

2

"Handy man!"

"ANY INSTRUCTIONS?"

"Relax."

"Wait till he's had his dinner."

"Take the bum out!"

"Refueling?"

1

". . . extends his regrets and wishes it known that for the next hour . . ."

2

"HOW *DO* YOU *DO*, HOW *DO* YOU *DO*, HOW . . ."

". . . do you do."

Ted Key

"Twelve hundred calories."

"Run across any tulips?"

"Madam chairman . . .

"ladies of the Teasdale Floral Society . . .

"and friends . . ."

1

2

3

1
"Who did this problem?"
2
"I did."
3
Ted Key
"Hundred per cent correct."

VETERINARIAN
Ted Key

"Breakfast's at eight."

"They're gone."

"And in this corner, wearing . . .

. . . Purple Trunks . . ."

"Through?"

"How's this sound? Roast stuffed turkey, potatoes, gravy, salad, onion soup, peas, string beans, tomato juice, cranberry sauce, celery, homemade biscuits, olives, pickles, blanched almonds, pumpkin pie and coffee."

"Knock it off!"

"He's being punished.
He can't come out."

"He's in his room!
He can't come out."

"Hi."

"Voting for who?"

"Not getting *MY* vote."

"... lack a shortstop, a catcher and a good first sacker.
On top of that, their pitching ..."

"Care to make a little side money?"

". . . six hundred and ten, six hundred and eleven, six hundred and twelve . . ."

Ted Key

Ted Key

"Now I've seen everything."

1

"Ladies present."

2

"Proceed."

"Slip showing."

"Lettuce?"

"Any more questions?"

"Hey, Musial!"

"Nonsense. What's a couple more at the dinner table? I'll tell Hazel now . . ."

". . . you're coming."

". . . or . . . better still—let's try that new restaurant near . . ."

Ted Key

"Coast's clear."

"A good friend of mine. Any more questions?"

"Eye dropper."

"MR. & MRS. DILL *AND* . . ."

"Set 'em up."

"Quiet!"

"First half."

"Papa loves Mambo—*UUH!*"

"I'll take the bum with the sequins."

"ICE CREAM!"

"I'll give you exactly *five* seconds."

"Look—I'll call you back."

"Not our bottles."

"What d'ya mean not your bottles!"

"Now *try* to eat something."

"But did you see him do it? No! We're getting sick and tired of you blaming our boy for everything that . . ."

"He's gone."

"Had enough?"

"Ninety-eight point six."

"B."
"E."
"D."
Ted Key

"Guess who's coming on her vacation!"

"BEE-ROTHER!"

"He's on his way, Mrs. Arthur."

"Now for the rebuttal."

"Anything else?"

"Hi ho, hi ho, it's off to school we go!"

"Some game!"

Ted Key

1
2
3
Ted Key

"When you're through with the paring knife—"

"Much of a struggle?"

"Take him off potatoes."

"He's coming."

"DOROTHY!"

"... right ... I'll tell her ... right ... yep ... I'll tell ..."

"Out of that refrigerator!!"

"Yep ... right ... I'll tell her ... right ..."

"If it's good enough for Lassie . . .!"

1
2
Ted Key

Ted Key

"OAKMONT HIGH!! CLASS OF THIRTY-ONE!!"

"YELLOW-bellied sapsucker!!"

"... down to get you in a taxi, honey ..."

"... BETTER BE READY 'BOUT HALF PAST EIGHT ..."

"You've been took."

"Dig *him!*"

1
2
Ted Key

"Nothing today."

G. WASHINGTON
Ted Key

BUBBLE GUM
Ted Key

"Bring 'er in."

Ted Key

"I wouldn't."

"They lead away from kings in the air force, major?"

"Who've they got? I'll tell you who they've got! They've got Mantle, they've got Yogi, they've got Turley, they've got Rizzuto, they've got . . ."

1.
2.
3.
4.
Ted Key
5.

"IN CLOSE!"

Ted Key

Ted Key

"Gentlemen."

"Anybody we know?"

"There are front yards, back yards, parks, playgrounds, alleys, attics, basements, playrooms, storerooms, lofts, garages, hundreds of sidewalks and thousands of lots. So *YOU . . .*"

1

2

"Early to bed,
Early to rise,
Makes a man healthy,
Wealthy and wise."

"Any law about turning on the heat?"

"Well, if you must know, on my next birthday I'll be exactly . . ."

"Come again?"

"Hungry?"

"Made your resolutions?"

"Care to join us?"

"Good silver?"

"Good morning, I represent . . ."

"*I'll* handle this."

"School burn down?"

"When you're through with the south forty . . ."

"Any luck?"

"Mr. Kroophead—Mrs. Kroophead—Mrs. Kroophead's sister—Mrs. Kroophead's brother—Lily Kroophead—Aggie Kroophead—Donald Kroophead—Sammy Kroophead and . . ."

". . . married to that bum, I'd lock him out too."

"Uh-oh . . ."

"... lots of sun, palm trees and coconuts. Heard St. Petersburg's nice. And Key West. Better turn over. They say Sarasota ..."

"At ease, men!"

"Hey, Ice Cream!!"

"You can say *THAT* again!"

". . . milk, bread, salt and get yourself an ice-cream cone. Now I'll repeat that. *IN THE ORDER OF THEIR IMPORTANCE*—milk, bread, salt and get yourself . . ."

"If I may turn the page . . ."

"Take your time. Circus will be here all week."

"Pay you next week! Inauguration!"

"One more word and *I'M* coming up there!"

"If I told you once, I told you a hundred times, *keep that lid on the grasshopper!*"

"Watch your step."

"Read where they unfroze wages . . ."

"So Scrooge gave his employee a *BIG, FAT BONUS,* and . . ."

"You'll write, of course."

"Auf Wiedersehen."

VETERINARIAN